EV_____ING
from the ROOTS

The Magic in the Work

Cindy Urbanski

Synergy Publishing Group
Belmont, NC

Evolving from the Roots: The Magic in the Work
Cindy Urbanski

Published by Synergy Publishing Group, Belmont, NC

Layout and design by Melisa Graham

Softcover, April 2024, ISBN 978-1-960892-20-1
E-book, April 2024, ISBN 978-1-960892-21-8

Dedication

To Bret, who excavated the roots I wanted to tend,
who has done the work of tending and evolving
alongside me for the past thirty years, and with
whom I get to share the magic of the work.
This is our love story.
Forever.

CONTENTS

Introduction

BULLDOZERS AND ROOTS

A bulldozer tears through the thick, unpassable underbrush clearing a path, jerking the blocking flora and fauna out by its roots, leaving them dangling in the air to wither and die, clearing a path. She wants to make the path more accessible for those she loves who are following behind. In this sense, bulldozing is a protective measure. And it's quite efficient. Woe be it to whatever, or even *whomever*, stands in the way.

When a girl resides in the dark, tangled underbrush, bulldozing can be effective to clear the path to get to spaces where the sun can shine. However, once that has been accomplished, bulldozing is no longer a necessary, or even useful, tool. The absolute devastation and destruction that she leaves in her wake is counterproductive to making the path accessible for herself and those she means to bring with her. In fact, she does just the opposite, throwing down debris and wreaking havoc.

I'm here to tell you that once the bulldozer shuts down her engines, some of those dangling roots find their way back into the earth, and a new, beautiful meadow of groundedness can emerge. If she has the courage to let go of her bulldozer persona for something softer and more nurturing, like a gardener, if she has the courage to let the roots find their way back, if she shows up to water them, a whole new growth of magical and quiet stillness can emerge where once there were roaring engines.

Her story of bulldozing is my story ....

There is a photo that I see first thing each morning and last thing each night on a dresser at the foot of my bed. It's a family photo from when my kids were small, and it's in my bedroom rather than the center of the house for a reason. Bret, my husband, and our two kids, Mackenzie and Mason, are huddled together on a blanket in the grass. The kids are both clinging to Bret, and all three of them are captured in full on giggles. I'm snuggled up beside them, looking at them. I am fit. My hair is amazing. I am smiling. But the smile doesn't reach my eyes. When I look at the picture, I see a woman longing to be a part of the joy in front of her. I see myself on the outside looking in. I see everything I had to lose in that moment. Oh I was a "part" of the family. I was helping raise the children, homeschooling my son, working at a local university, and working on my PhD. I was getting a ton of work done, and I would have said I was doing all of this for my family, but I was simply going, doing, running, bulldozing. I was not engaged with them as people.

Photo by Jennifer Fagan

Later, probably even a couple of years after that photo was taken, I started to do the work of shutting down the bulldozer so that I could stop being an outsider looking in on all that joy. It was a long journey. It *is* a long journey. That photo stays there not only so I can begin each day with the beauty of my family, but also to remind me of why I slow down and do "the work," even (and especially) on days when it feels impossible.

I still fear the camera for what will be reflected in the lens. And yet, in October of 2022, a decade after that family photo was taken, I talked myself into a yoga photo shoot. At the time, I had left academia and become a 500-hour certified yoga teacher. In that process, I committed myself to living yoga *in* my life, not just on my mat. I needed photos to document that shift for myself as well as for marketing purposes. I talked myself into being photographed by imagining that my now-grown kids would do it with me. Easy. Fun. But Mackenzie was in the midst of her senior year at a college in another city, and Mason was not all that excited about the idea of being photographed in his yoga practice. ("Mom, that's just weird!") So when the day came, it was just me.

Thankfully, Mason agreed to come with me once I was transparent about my nerves over the whole thing. That was my first act of rootedness that day. The transparency. The result was exhilarating. Not only was my eighteen-year-old son happy to be my wardrobe dude, but when my mind was a terrified blank, he also reminded me of postures I love. And standing there in all of his glory, giving me all of the support, he gave me something to really smile about.

We took the pictures deep in the forest with my bare feet on the earth, where I feel most grounded. I was rooted. I practiced my breathing. I gave myself over to the photographer, my son, and the yoga. I played.

The result is a portfolio of pictures capturing pure joy. The photographer posted on social media, and strangers commented on that joy. My friends exclaimed over how grounded, powerful, and downright joyful I look in these images. My husband, the truth teller, commented on the "real smiles." They are, indeed, evidence of my commitment to yoga as life.

Photo by Wanda Koch

Now, alongside the picture I began my story with, is a photo from that shoot that explodes with joy. It reminds me of the journey. It reminds me to shut down the bulldozer and remain rooted in the only work that matters, the work of staying in the moment and pausing in the magic in each of these moments. The work does not equate with perfectionism. I don't have to be a perfect parent or partner. I don't need a perfect body or career. I don't have to create the perfect vacation, party, or holiday. I just have to commit to the practice of showing up and doing life the best way I know how in the moment, going to my edge, getting stronger, growing constantly, falling down, messing up, dusting off, and getting back to the practice of re-engaging. For me, perfectionism is the bulldozer.

At its core, my story is about what happened when one woman stopped bulldozing … stopped running away from fear and guilt and shame, from the past and even disease, and stopped pushing toward perfectionism and an image of what she "should" be. It's about what happened when I stopped working so very hard all of the time and rooted myself in the work. This is a book about being still and how that brought me to a place where I could practice radical acceptance *most* days. In that opening image, I was bulldozing my way through life. Eventually, I learned that bulldozing was not only unsustainable but also unnecessary at best and destructive at worst. This book is about *that* evolution beginning at the root.

The second picture, my yoga in the woods picture, captures the joy that comes with staying grounded, or as I like to think of it, staying rooted because roots go deep into the ground, and I have been healing at the root in order to become grounded. It is something I practice moment by moment.

I continue the journey each day when I wake up and my eyes land on those pictures. Life has often been wild, and the lessons for me in the necessity of stillness abound. The bulldozer revs its engine still in the tough moments of life. I have to intentionally shut it off and find ease in what is happening around me. It's a practice. On the regular, I have to recognize that crazy and wild though things might be, lack of sleep and lack of a walk/yoga schedule is not sustainable for my mental health. I get out my chock-full calendar and carve out time for regular walks and yoga for the next month. I make space and let go of some stuff. I want to do all the things for all the people, but if I don't take care of myself, I take care of no one, becoming a bulldozer instead, leaving devastation in my path. When I let go, I can show up grounded and rooted in the presence of what is needed!

In order to remind me to shut down the bulldozer, I start and end each day with something called a "loving kindness prayer," given to me by my yoga teacher, Johnna Smith. I offer it up to the universe. Now, I would like to offer it to us, both myself as the writer of this book and you as the reader. This is my dearest wish for us.

May we be happy.
May no harm come to us.
May we be joyful.
May we be at peace.

Because ... life is a practice.

I spent forty years bulldozing my way through life in order to take care of my people and the world. I've spent the last decade cultivating my roots. I'm fifty years old. I'm not "there," and I hope I will be on the journey of evolving forever.

After posting a bit of writing from the book you hold here to a trusted group as an act of putting myself out there in all my vulnerability, two women I've known for over twenty years said, "You are an Evolution, and this goes deep into who you already were at your core." So here I am, evolving at the root. I invite you to start an evolution with me as you read this series of essays describing that evolution from a bulldozer to a woman who strives to do the work and, in so doing, has found her magic!

The essays in this series are connected, but not. They work on their own and as a whole. They can be read in order, or as needed in the right moment. Journeys often don't follow a straight path. The path moves over, around, and through, sometimes doubling back on itself in time and space. The path is messy rather than neatly linear, and it is my intention to reflect that in the structure of this book.

Part 1

WATERING THE ROOTS

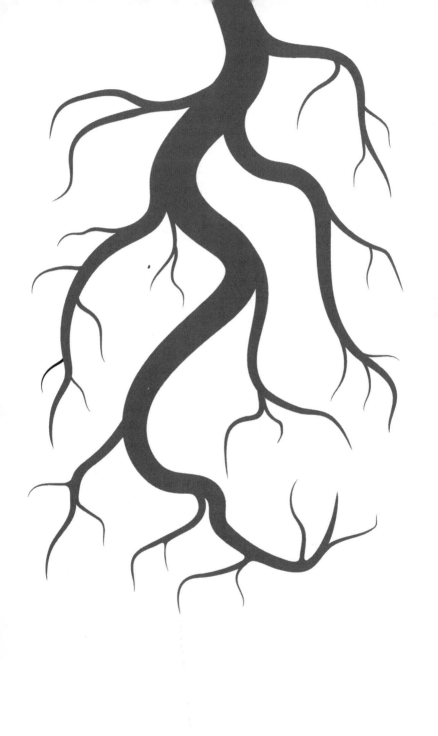

THE MAGIC OF
THE PAUSE

Twenty years ago, I tentatively dipped my toes in the blissful waters of the pause as I struggled on my mat through *savasana* (Sanskrit for "corpse pose" and the final pose in most yoga practices where you lie on the floor in stillness) at the end of practice. My grandmother, Nellie Rollins, never did a yoga pose in her life and certainly didn't truck with "magic," but in truth, she was a skilled practitioner of both, and one of my very first teachers. I would do well to keep listening to her gentle whisper in my ear, and yes, I still hear her even though she's been gone for those same twenty years. When I tune in, she says, "Slow down, dear one. Stop. Lock eyes. Listen more. Talk less. Be still. Be present. Relish each moment."

She's right.

She's trying to remind me to shut down revving engines of the bulldozer.

My grandmother was a beautiful, graceful woman. She made shirtwaist dresses look stunning, and I swear she had one in every color with shoes and a purse to match. These were her office, church, and visiting clothes. For working around the house or with her flowers and animals, she wore matching button up shirts and what she called "tough slacks." They were cotton and, like the dresses, came in all colors of the rainbow.

While she was beautiful, she wasn't fussy. She got up each morning, put her hair into quick pin curls, wrapped a bright scarf around her head, and headed to the kitchen. She kept lipstick in the half bath by the back door and quickly applied it without looking as she headed out to feed her chickens and gather the eggs in the predawn light. She'd return, make a full breakfast, change, brush the curls, and be out the door to go to the office of the family car parts business or to church, looking effortlessly put together.

The lipstick for chicken care still puzzles me. Yet it made her look like a movie star. The value of a little lipstick clearly made an impression on me as a child, and yet, I struggle to make lip gloss happen before a Zoom meeting. Goals.

There was magic in the way my grandmother moved; even when she was in full-on "go," there was a sense of pause. With all six of us grandchildren (including my brother and my four cousins) and my grandfather in the house for Saturday morning breakfast, a spread for sure,

she moved with complete calm. Let me tell you.
It takes my brother, my father, *and* me all moving
at full speed on Christmas morning to pull off the
breakfast that she used to serve up on any given
Saturday. I mean, let's think about it. Getting
grits, scrambled eggs, country ham with gravy,
and biscuits for ten or more hungry people to all
come to the table at the same time, piping hot,
is a three-person job. And yet the woman floated
around her kitchen with a song on her lips and
not an ounce of flour on the floor, pulling it off
with all of us underfoot. The magic was in being
completely present in the moment, in never
allowing herself to be rushed, but instead pausing
often to relish every one of life's moments.

Grandma was simply unflappable. She could
glide from one room to the next with a cup of
coffee full to the brim without spilling a drop.
And if a copperhead were to show up in our yard,
she would use the same gait to arrive at our house
next door, hoe over her shoulder, to dispense with
said snake with a single chop behind the head and
then hang it in a tree to warn all the other snakes.
All without any fuss. Now, I can dispense with a
snake with the same precision, but I must admit it
is accompanied by a lot more squealing and a lot
less calm.

All that said, my very favorite image of my
elegant grandmother is from the time my

grandfather thought we needed turkeys. They grew into huge, wild things, and they did not take kindly to the small coop in which they were kept. They were just plain mean, and they went on the offensive if anyone entered their area, flying directly at the person's head. We are talking around twenty-five pounds of angry bird, wings spread, in full attack. My grandma was the one who fed them and picked up the giant eggs. We grandchildren *loved* this ritual. The six of us would line up outside the coop to watch the show. She would enter, gracefully and calmly, with a shovel over her shoulder, and when one of those birds inevitably came at her, she would swing that shovel at its head like a samurai warrior and send it sailing, while remaining completely nonplussed. She would look at the stunned bird, nod her head once, and then go about the business of feeding and egg collecting.

Though these stories from the yard are etched in my mind, it's my grandmother's yellow kitchen that is a central image in my childhood. It was the place where I came with all of my scraped knees, be they literal or metaphorical. It was my safe haven, the place where I knew everything would be okay, where whatever existential crisis I was having at the moment would be solved.

It's no wonder that I find peace, now, in my own blue kitchen. It is my dream kitchen, renovated to meet my wildest culinary dreams. In it, I find my Zen in creating something delectable and nutritious all at the same time. It's space in my insanely busy world. It's the place where my children and others find me to talk and to solve problems. It's a place of safety because I'm not a perfectionist here. It's just cooking. If it doesn't turn out, there's always peanut butter and homemade jam. Heck, I am the same girl who made chicken gravy once a week when I was first married and threw it out every week for the first year because it was inedible. I just kept trying until I created something that tasted good. So, in many ways, I've created a space and a pause for myself ... and others. Yet despite all of the grace and space I have created in my kitchen, thanks to what my grandmother modeled, I can still feel something is missing.

I take a lot of pride in the work I do in my kitchen. Homemade jams, yogurt, bone broth, and canned vegetables, even homemade dog food, are balm to my soul. Knowing that I am nourishing my people with the best possible things, made fresh with my own hands, brings a sense of calm. I've always been this way. When Mackenzie started eating solid food at six months old, I made it all from fresh vegetables, cooking and pureeing and freezing it in ice trays. When we adopted Mason at two, and he came to us suffering from malnutrition, I carefully crafted foods that he would eat and that would make him strong and healthy. I cultivated his palette to accept the fresh fruit and vegetables that were so foreign to him. Later, I planned and connived to create healthy family dinners even when both kids were actively involved in various sports and activities as teenagers. Sometimes those dinners were eaten in the back of my old 4-Runner, but they were made by my hands out of real food.

But here's the thing. I cook like I'm in a hurricane. To have me in your kitchen (and I will gladly take over any kitchen anywhere) is to have it turned upside down and covered in whatnot.

So here's the missing piece ....

My grandmother would turn off all of the pots, stop mixing the next cake batter, and sit down with a soothing beverage in a chair when I showed up with tears in my eyes, slamming the back door and needing to talk. It was more than a pause. It was a hard stop. Everything, including getting dinner on the table for anyone who might show up and after Grandma had put in a full day of work for the family car parts business, ceased except me. Time was not an issue. It meant nothing. I meant everything.

So, as I think about it, her kitchen is where that stop began and is the image that looms large in my mind, but the other central place of safety was her wood-paneled den. Grandma would take her orange, pleather seat with matching footstool, and I would perch on the footstool of the green chair with the six-foot, mounted mahi-mahi my grandfather once caught on the wall behind it. While I barely let my rear touch the cushion and vibrated with a child's anxiety or teen-aged righteous indignation, or later the hyperattentive exhaustion of a new mother, my grandmother exuded complete peace and calm. No. Matter. What. And over the thirty years that I had her in my life, I brought a truckload of "what" to her.

My grandmother wasn't a talker or a fixer. She was an intense listener. She would hold her mug between her hands, totally relax into the chair, put her feet up, and listen for as long as I needed to talk. She would lock eyes with me. I *had* to look this woman in the eye and share my story. Hers were always soft and understanding. They lacked judgment and exuded acceptance. She made it easy.

That's what I remember. Her words were usually succinct and reassuring. "Everything is going to work out. It's all okay." Something along those lines. What mattered then, and what matters in the example she set for me, is that I *believed* her. Not because of the words, but because I felt 100 percent heard and safe.

The den moment is what I am missing. My kitchen is a pause in my overactive brain, and a place where my children and others come for solace, but I do not stop. All too often, I still don't turn off the pots and ignore time, walk to a well-worn chair and sit down. I don't lock eyes with the other person often enough.

Pausing and stopping are hard for me. Like *really* hard. I am in constant motion from the time I wake up until I fall asleep at night. I mentioned savasana at the opening of this essay. Here's a secret. I skipped savasana most days for a decade before I made myself do it. It's still the hardest pose of any practice. Cooking in my sunny kitchen is indeed a pause, but I'm still moving. Chopping, stirring, the things one does in a kitchen. Moving meditation is a thing. It's why fast, hot yoga appeals to me so much. But I'm starting to recognize that stillness is magical, both for me and for my people. It's the ability to remove the clock and just be squarely in the moment.

My grandmother was showing me how to serve myself as well as my people. She always looked like she relished those moments with me. Maybe because it was time with her granddaughter, but I think it was because she knew the power of a true pause. She had the wherewithal to set aside time and to-dos for her people. And it wasn't like I was the only one who was showing up at her door. She had six grandchildren living right next to her. The house was a revolving door of her children and grandchildren, all seeking her guidance and wisdom. And, without a doubt, any person that walked in would be met with amazing smells wafting from the oven and the stove, their favorite beverage, and her undivided attention. They'd be met with magic.

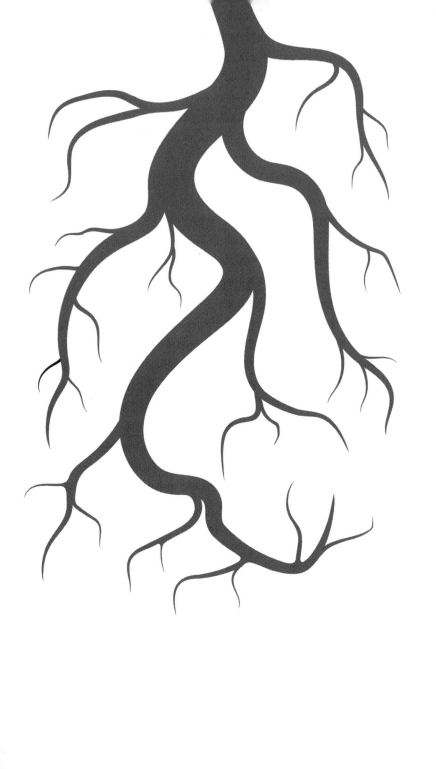

CRYSTAL BALLS, DISCIPLINE, AND FREEDOM

My husband is a dedicated listener to the podcaster and former Navy Seal Jocko, who says, "Discipline equals freedom." Now, I can get behind that. I've spent many a day grinding out workouts, grinding out tasks in my job and life out of pure discipline, believing that it makes me "good." But that grinding out is not what I'm talking about and not what I would posit Jocko means. I'm talking about something a little softer, a little truer for me. I'm speaking of discipline in the way my grandma modeled it. Discipline is less about the hustle and more about making a clear choice of correct action. Not simply "hustling" for the sake of hustling, but doing the thing that we know is correct for *us* as individual humans. *That* discipline equals freedom.

I shared this bit of thinking with my husband, and he pushed me to say more about the "freedom" part of the equation. You see, freedom is not the "stuff" one "gets" from a life of discipline, of finding the priorities and dealing with them in order, leaving the lower priorities for later. It's the freedom of resting in the knowledge that one has chosen the most precious priorities and has relieved oneself of the hooks of the ones that don't matter. My husband called this the "knife point" that society can hold us to if we allow it. When we have the discipline to "stop" (or pause), to *identify* the priorities, we get to experience true freedom.

I like to think of priorities as the crystal balls in my juggling act of life. Those crystal balls are the most important, fragile things that need all of my focus, because if I drop them, they will shatter. The other things on the list that aren't my chosen priorities, yet need doing, are rubber balls. On good days, I allow those rubber balls that look like a "should," whether those are created by society or my story of self, to fall and bounce away under the sofa with the dust bunnies that tend to reside there. That's when I feel the full equation in its most pure form: discipline equals freedom.

Juggling crystal balls and freedom have shown up many times in my life. Let me explain.

On an Embodied Writing Experience retreat, my colleague and I were leading a group of heart-centered folk into the embodied writing of the books they had inside them. We were on beautiful Amelia Island, and it was a 70-degree day in February that year. The huge deck of our gorgeous house overlooked the ocean where the sun rises. Magic.

And So. Much. Discipline.

Day one was a full day of writing. Part of my role there was to be the nourisher, and at lunch time, when I entered the kitchen, no one even looked up. I set out some snacks and left them alone. As a group, we churned out words and wrote through hard things until I finally called a hard stop at 6 p.m. because dinner was ready and hot, and I didn't want it to get cold. We had been writing since 9 a.m. The only words I have to describe the look of these folks was shell-shocked. Everyone went to their rooms and to bed by 8:30 p.m. Grinding out words is discipline, as our culture recognizes it.

And then we woke up. I was awake at 6 a.m., mind a-swirl about what I had been writing and the grocery list. (We had forgotten a few items, and I wanted to get them before anyone woke up.) I made my coffee and put on my clothes, ready to get the chore out of the way, ready to return quickly to then grind out some more words, when the beautiful Laura came up the stairs. When I say she is beautiful, I mean this woman glows with life and joy and love for the world. With power.

Laura is the owner and brain trust of an amazing holistic company worth a shit ton of money. She birthed her company out of a deep desire to birth a baby and save the world. She is the real deal. She is grounded and solid and in tune. She teaches people to connect with their bodies and listen intently to what their bodies have to say. She heals. She is disciplined. Yet she was a swirl of emotion when she came up the stairs. I was about to hustle out of the door on my way to get groceries before yoga (aka, do the things) when I heard my grandmother whisper "pause." Laura needed to unload some stuff. I listened to my grandmother and made another cup of coffee, even though my "get er' done" monkey mind was screaming otherwise.

In my pausing, I was blessed with Laura's humanness. Her dog had recently died. She thought her son might be on the spectrum, or maybe not. Maybe it was just a result of COVID isolation. She would love her son the same no matter what, but the not knowing phase they were in at the time was hard beyond words. He was two and a half. He wasn't talking. The world said he should have been. She knew all the things about early childhood development and how these things come in their own time, *and* she was worried. She was wondering if she'd ever hear this precious boy say, "Mama." She knew how to go inside, to ground, to "just be." She'd woken up too early after a fitful night, and then had drifted off again. She wanted to see the sunrise. She set an alarm. She fell back into a blissful sleep, and then the alarm went off. She had to talk to herself. Her monkey mind was screaming "go back to sleep," but her wise mind knew that she needed to see that sunrise. She got up. She stumbled to the kitchen. She was human. And then she did indeed see the sun rise. She held tightly to the crystal ball: connection. That was the magic we *both* needed.

I went on to the grocery store, heart lighter, moving more slowly, feeling time as abundance. My daughter called from college, and we had a lovely chat while I picked things off of the shelves. Like Laura, Mackenzie didn't need anything other than to connect. I was working my list and slowed down even more to attend to her stories of physics lab partners and lunch plans. It took a little longer, but I managed to procure everything on the list along with an "I love you" from my child who had flown the nest. The one I know will never claim my address as "permanent" again. The one who brings me joy because of the sheer size of her wing span. The one who calls almost daily just as I'm starting my to-do list, just to chat. She fills me with joy and reminds me in a tangible way just about every day that if I pause and chat, I will be blessed.

When I returned to the retreat house, the writers were up and moving in anticipation of yoga. Everyone, it seems, had a rough night. Minds simply wouldn't shut down. Everyone had been awake before dawn and needed breakfast. So we adjusted the schedule to make space for that.

Now, I must stop here to talk about how *big* of a deal that is for me. I live for a good schedule. I was a high school teacher for over a decade, and those bells marking time brought me great peace. I have s.t.r.u.g.g.l.e.d with my time gremlins. So. Very. Much. The appointed time for yoga came, and I calmly said, "Eat; we will adjust." And I felt peace. Because it was right. We would get to yoga when we got to it, and then the writing day would begin. People needed to eat. I am the nourisher, *and* I am the yoga instructor.

The ten-minute delay (yep, I was making a big deal out of ten measly minutes) gifted us with sun warming the deck, so we moved our practice outside, with the ocean crashing as our music, the sun caressing our faces. We chose a restorative practice. Five-minute holds in predominantly supine positions. Nobody's Apple watch was congratulating them on their exercise or activity ring. Just peace and being in our bodies. A coming back to who we were as individuals and why we had made this space to write, to show up for ourselves.

Finally, we came together to begin the day of writing. More bowls of oatmeal, berries, and granola came out. We reached for our notebooks, ready to get going with the writing we were there for, with the words and ideas that kept us up all night. And Shana, our leader, stopped us yet again. She asked us to take everything out of our hands. She asked us to ground down on our sitz bones and feet, if they were on the floor. She led us through a beautiful five-minute meditation that I'll call "Just Be." In my mind, I saw the image of a tree, pliable and swaying in the storms of life with roots planted safely and firmly. I was again blessed with stillness. And then Laura— the beautiful Laura, Shana's teacher—gifted us all again. After I had shared my very grounded image, she bravely said, "What came up for me was, 'Shana, you bitch! Fuck you for holding me to my own best practices. I struggled to 'just be.' And I fought it hard. And then I was." Crystal balls are what ground us. The rubber ones are often what scatter us to the winds.

Now, it can be easier, at least for me, to isolate true priorities when on "retreat," so I want to touch on one more "real life" example.

It had been a tough week, and it was only Wednesday. Facing me on my calendar for the day were back-to-back appointments, one for physical therapy and one for emotional therapy.

I was recovering from a back injury, and I had an unrelated anxiety attack earlier in the week that had me reaching out for an emergency session with my therapist.

I didn't want to go to either appointment. Not even a little bit.

My back was feeling 100 percent better, and as a yoga instructor, I felt like I "mostly" knew what to do to keep it healthy. And the appointment was going to take time, a precious commodity around here.

Therapy was going to be an emotional slog. A couple of days had passed since the episode that had me reaching out, and I was feeling more or less back on my limb. This appointment, too, was going to take time plus a lot of emotional work.

I had to take a moment and really look at the priorities. My family is priority one. That said, I also know that I can't take care of them if I don't care for myself, and self-care was badly needed. So while physical therapy and emotional therapy together were going to take about three hours away from the time I could be working with my family, it had to happen. I had to dig deep and be disciplined enough to prioritize myself and the things I really didn't want to do but were absolutely necessary in order to prioritize the people I most cherish.

Crystal balls. Without physical health and strength, I can't practice yoga, which is key to my mental health. Without my mental health, I'm no good to anyone. And hiding out and using my family as an excuse not to focus on my mental health is not going to cut it.

In the end, I went to physical therapy and worked up a deep core routine that I can include in my yoga and walking rituals. I had to swallow my ego and recognize that while I am very strong in my upper body and legs, my core is screaming for attention. I went to emotional therapy where, while very difficult, I learned more about myself and trauma responses and how to head off triggers. It's deep work where, again, I had to check my ego at the door because I was pretty sure I had "handled" my past trauma.

I walked away from those three hours humbled and free. I had a plan to strengthen my core and support my back. I had a plan to head off further episodes of mental breakdown in their tracks. I felt powerful and in control of my life because I knew I did the right things. And I knew that those right things would benefit my people. I was not trapped by my back or my mental state. I was free. The crystal balls were safe, and the rubber ones were bouncing merrily away.

Part 2

FINDING THE MAGIC IN THE WORK

RUNNING AWAY
FROM THE WORK

The following showed up in my Facebook memories from 2009 as I was writing this book in 2022:

> *I am wondering how we eradicate the fiction of a dichotomy between work and play.*

I wish I could say that I figured out the solution. In reality, this was some academic nonsense that I never really took to heart. Until now. The year, 2022, had been about burning down and redefining the idea of the words "work" and "retreat" and, yes, "play." I was *seeking* when I shared that post on Facebook. That's why that line moved me enough to pontificate on social media. But I was not *finding*. Work, retreats, and conferences, and the idea of play that came with them were filled with toxicity. Not because life as a teacher and academic, or even playing, is toxic, but because of my approach to all three. These events brought shame and guilt and righteous indignation with them. Finally, in 2022 the veil lifted, and I have come to enjoy new definitions of the words that fill me up rather than tear me down. The burning down and rebirth has come to pass all because I stopped running away and began to focus on the idea that discipline equals freedom.

My tendency toward running away began when Mackenzie was a year old. That would have been 2002. For the first six months of her life, I was in a blissful, baby haze. Bret was new in the financial planning business, and I had taken a year's leave of absence from teaching. Mackenzie was born on June 18, 2001, two weeks after school ended. I spent the first six months breastfeeding every two hours, writing my first book during nap times, and sitting on the floor beside her, organizing Bret's files. He worked late many evenings, and we would join him at the bank after it closed at five and bang out a couple more hours of filing, paperwork, and emails to build his client base.

Mackenzie was a pretty easy baby as long as I was in her line of sight. If I left the room, she would scream. If I left the house, God help anyone who was left with her. I would leave bottles of carefully pumped breast milk, which she would refuse, going on a hunger strike until I returned. And for those first six months, I really didn't mind. We were inseparable. And then on September 11, the world rocked. While I was horrified and devastated, strangely, I wasn't totally thrown off kilter. The day it happened, I thought, "Okay, Bret is going to sign up to fight a war, die, and leave me a single mother. That is going to suck, and I'm going to be really sad, but I've got this." Worst-case scenario thinking (or catastrophizing I've learned through therapy) is the way my mind works when I don't monitor it carefully. I always go to the absolute worst thing that could happen, make a plan, and then resolve that I'm "fine." Now, I know this is not healthy, imagining the worst all the time. But it does keep me calm when the unthinkable happens. It's an old coping mechanism that doesn't *really* serve me anymore. I'm a work in progress, not a sage.

At around six months, two things happened. Mackenzie started to crawl, and she started to eat some solid foods. The feedings were spread out, and she was mobile. And I started to miss teaching and went a little stir crazy. I don't remember the exact moment; I just remember sort of awaking from a haze around the six-month mark and thinking, "I need to be around bigger people. I need to teach."

So, as I had always done, I got my butt in gear working out a way to do that. Full-time seemed like more time away from Mackenzie than I could handle. Don't let anybody fool you: teaching high school full-time is easily an eighty hour a week gig. Teaching 180 students how to write eats up a lot of time. Fortunately, a teacher who had been at the high school I was on maternity leave from was ready to retire, but not completely ready to give it all up. The principal wanted both of us, so he said we could split a position. I had the best of both worlds. I taught half days, and therefore worked sane hours. I was leaving the house around 8 a.m. and returning by 4 p.m. each day, rather than the 5:30 a.m. to 5 p.m. hours I'd kept when I taught full-time.

The promise of the job and then the job itself was enough for a while. Mackenzie also grew big enough to fit in the jogging stroller at six months, so we—Mackenzie, Doc (the yellow lab), and I— logged a lot of miles. Like the dog, the pounding speed kept me from losing my mind and tearing down the proverbial walls.

But then, in January, after I started back to work in August, I was coming apart at the seams. I felt like I was losing my mind. I started fantasizing again about living by myself on Ocracoke Island with some cats, my old dream from before I met Bret. I was unspeakably sad about the whole thing. I adored my daughter and husband and the life we had built, but something was just off. I was miserable, often feeling like I was going to fly into a thousand pieces. Some days I was full of energy, mastering the to-dos like a boss. Other days, I could barely get out of bed.

Martin Luther King weekend of that year was the first time I ran away. I was convinced that what I needed was a break from people. I just wanted to be and read and write and run without anyone or anything dictating my schedule. I'm pretty sure that there are plenty of young, working mothers with this desire, but I wonder how many of them want to do it alone. I did not have the courage to be honest with myself. The truth was, I wanted to hide from my shame and hide from not being blissfully happy with what looked like a perfect life. In fact, I flat out lied to myself. I convinced myself that I just needed a break, and that this need was completely normal. I wanted to be away, in my own space, in my own head. There was so much scrambled there; I wanted to have some quiet and some peace to sort it out. Again, a normal desire except for hiding and shame over the scramble. I talked to Bret about needing a break, and though he was confused and hurt by my request, and somewhat dubious I think, he agreed that I should go.

At the time, I thought that I chose a poor spot. I wanted to check myself into a hotel for the weekend, but Bret, ever watchful of our pennies and very resourceful, sent me to my grandparents' lake house. I blamed the space. It was big and empty and cold and haunted by memories of my family, but in hindsight, I would have reacted the same to being anywhere alone. I was afraid of what was in my head. I simply could not be there. The scramble and misery were agonizing. And the guilt, oh the guilt. I had left my perfect daughter and husband. I had the perfect life. I had a wonderful man who worshiped me and a funny, easy baby who was pure delight. I had the choice to work part-time at a job I loved. What the heck was there to be so miserable about? Yet there I sat, looking at the water through the cloudy sliding glass door, sitting in the red vinyl rocking chair, sobbing as if my heart were broken.

The moment I was away from Bret and Mackenzie, I felt none of the relief I was expecting. I was bereft. I worried about how the two of them would get along without me. Would Mackenzie get the right naps, and would she eat the right foods? Would they have fun? Would they even miss me? I sure as heck missed them. So I did what I always did when I needed an escape; I read, and I wrote, and I ran. All of these things felt productive and right. And they are. People should read more books and write more things and move their bodies. I felt righteous doing these things because they were "good." But I couldn't settle in and enjoy any of them, because I was lying to myself. Although good in theory, none of these things were good, righteous, or healthy for me at the time because I was simply using them as an escape, as a way to ignore the chaos in my mind. Of course, when I stopped reading and writing and running, the chaos was still there.

So as soon as the sun went down, which happens blissfully early in January, I opened a bottle of wine. Again, not that out of the ordinary, or so I told myself, but the lie was still there; I was still metaphorically running as hard and as fast as I could. I slept fitfully and got up the next morning feeling sluggish and more out of sorts than when I arrived. But I lied to myself again, saying this getaway had been great, just what I needed. I had carved out a little time alone to do the things I wanted to do without interruption.

I went home and rejoined my family, but instead of being refreshed and filled up, I was tired, cranky, and a mess. Routine has always soothed me, so I was looking forward to getting back into the rhythm of work after the long weekend. But it snowed, daycare was closed, and I was pretty sure I was *really* going to lose my mind.

Bret and I negotiated, and he worked from home with Mackenzie while I went into school to get out of the house and grade papers. I told a friend, an older woman who was a mother figure to me, that I had "run away" for the weekend. I said it in a light-hearted, flippant way, but this woman had a bullshit detector like no other. She simply looked at me and said, "Well, I'm glad you came back." I was exposed like a raw nerve. I shuffled away and buried myself in work, once again putting up my shield of armor and pretending to everyone and myself that everything was "fine." I had it all under control. Nothing was wrong. My life was perfect.

Over the years, I would become the master at running away in ways I disguised to myself as "legitimate" because the leaves were related to "work." I went to conferences, workshops, and writing retreats. I flew around the country. I stopped asking Bret what he thought about these excursions and just submitted proposals, announced when I was accepted, and hit the road. Again, on the surface, this is perfectly normal activity for an academic. The problem was the underlying running away and escape I was seeking each time I did it. A glass of wine with a burger and fries became a ritual in all airports. Conferences and writing retreats meant heavy drinking. We were a bunch of writers after all.

Over time, Bret, as is his way, started to pick up on the unhealthy nature of these journeys. He was on to me, and it caused a lot of tension between us. I was working, I claimed. He just didn't want me to work, I thought. He was being controlling, I decided. I was angry each time I left because "he" made me feel guilty. But in reality, I was the one creating all of the guilt. It was there, hiding under the surface. He was angry that I was hiding. Things were tense between us for weeks each time a trip or any discussion of a trip approached.

Things finally came to a head one February when I had the honor of reading the site profiles for the National Writing Project, an organization that supports teachers and students with writing initiatives. I was over the moon at being asked and never discussed it with Bret. I just announced casually that I would be gone for five days and that he would be in charge of the kids (Mason had come into our lives by this point). While I was there, I even said to the friend I was rooming with, "They don't need me anymore; they are all perfectly fine without me." This was the first inkling of my thinking that my family was better off without me. I only valued myself for the things I could do for them, like laundry and cooking, and they had shown that they could handle that alone.

I came home to a very different story. Bret had had it with my traveling that was only increasing and involving less and less discussion between us. I remember him saying, "That's it, no more trips," which pissed me off because how dare he tell me what to do. But that's the thing. He would never tell me what to do. This was a "popping sound in the Fire Swamp" moment, but I didn't notice.

I changed his words and got angry, not really hearing what he was saying and creating in my mind that I was being controlled.

During the spring of 2020, during the purging that happened in my house because we were stuck there, I found the following note from Bret. It came with sheet music for Evanescence's "My Immortal":

> *Honeybun–*
>
> *So I was listening to this song on the iPod the other day, and I was struck. The darkest parts of it reminded me of our most difficult moments and circumstances. During these [moments], we discussed that you sometimes feel you are a burden and that maybe we would all be better off without you around here. I have always known that that would never be the case because my life is so right because of who you are as an individual and who we are as parents, soulmates, yin & yang, Laurel and Hardy.*
>
> *Just the same, I was struck. The message is hard hitting. I gave you everything, I supported you, yet you just keep hanging on, you make pain; there's just too much that time cannot erase. How very wrong!! There will never be a reason to throw in the towel. There is no mountain too tall to overcome*

together. Time's will is bent to our bidding
because we do not know what defeat would
be. Our wounds always heal; pain means
real life is real. You are my immortal, the
better side of me, the complement I was once
without, my fresh new pair of socks.

So I re-wrote the meaning of the song to
me, and every time I hear it, I feel that I am
stronger, smarter, and better. And I am, too,
because of who I am when we are me and
you. Love Immortal.

This letter is dated December 2008. The
aforementioned February trip was earlier that
same year.

Though the note was lost in the files for so long,
I do remember getting it as a Christmas present,
and I can tell you I was very shocked and put
back on my heels on the defensive. I remember
leaving the family gift circle and angry crying in
the bathroom. You see, rather than reading it as
the testament to true, unconditional partnership
and love that it is, I skipped completely over the
part about rewriting the meaning of the song
and was crushed by guilt because of the original
lyrics. In all that he said, all that my befuddled
mind read was, "The message is hard hitting. I
gave you everything, I supported you, yet you
just keep hanging on, you make pain, there's just

too much that time cannot erase." My reaction to Bret's adoring note is typical of what my brain did in those days. It deleted all of the good, all of the compliments, all of the thank yous, and isolated the (made up, actually) criticism. It solidified that I was a big burden on everyone in my home.

Twelve years would pass, and I wouldn't be able to hear the song without bursting into tears. Reading Bret's words again when I found them, I burst into fresh tears realizing that I had completely missed how wonderful and committed my husband was even in the midst of some of our darkest, most confusing times. Had I been able to wrap my head around his commitment then, it would have saved a tremendous amount of pain and heartache.

I am drafting the chapter you are reading on the last day of a retreat. The sun is about to rise, and I've shown up out here to see nature's show with words swirling in my head. Yesterday, I cooked three meals, taught yoga, wrote, and played on the beach. I meditated in the afternoon sun with a bottle of homemade kombucha beside me. I am at "work." And I am filled up to the brim rather than worn out and empty. Bret and Mason are at home, and I can't wait to see them. I feel free. The shame gremlins haven't shown their ugly heads.

What changed? I stopped running away. I had the courage to tell myself the truth and stop lying and hiding. I am living in the open, and I have surrounded myself with people who do the same. Ironically, some of the participants of the retreat happen to also be people who were in my life and closest to me when I was running away years ago, which tells me, it had little to do with the people and everything to do with me.

Bret and I discussed this retreat for hours, deciding if it was right for our family. It had been on the calendar with question marks beside it up until mere days before I left. We were patient and in conversation and searching to see if it was a correct, disciplined choice.

We, the retreat leaders and I, have created a spaciousness around this experience that allows for discipline in the form of right choices for each individual. As the nourisher, I planned wholesome, clean meals for us all to enjoy. The food has been plentiful and filling, and to eat it has been to love on one's body.

I have offered yoga every morning. Everyone has shown up, but no one did it out of compulsion; it was simply a right choice. And I tailored the yoga to what I was seeing and feeling from each of our clients each morning. What did we need? What music did we need to hear to fill us up? How did we need to move our bodies? I studied it all, and then made a disciplined choice. And in turn, people came in and out of poses as they needed to, the right choices for them.

Days were spent writing words and getting real, honest feedback, but at some point, each person would say to themselves, "Enough," and go for a walk on the beach, to further move their bodies and clear their heads. Evenings involved a glass of wine for some, not all, but it was a nurturing act and not an attempt to obliterate or escape. Each night ended early, and folks were in their own rooms by 8 p.m.

Right choices. Crystal balls kept safe!

As the retreat drew to a close, I felt that I had bridged that gap between work and play by doing the actual work. It's about being present and real in what you are doing, be that work or play. It's about putting your real self out in the open for yourself and the people around you. It's about right choices and the discernment about what is a crystal ball and what is a rubber ball. The freedom and the absolute magic is in staying in the moment and doing the work rather than running from it.

RUNNING TO
THE WORK

After a decidedly unathletic childhood, and a flirtation with step aerobics in college, I started running at the age of twenty-two because the high school where I had my first teaching gig needed an assistant cross-country coach who was a woman, and my husband and I needed money. What started as walk/runs for a couple of miles with Doctor, my faithful yellow lab, turned into my first four-mile run through the sewer trail (yep, you read that correctly) with the cross-country team. The team cheered me on and pushed me the whole way. I lay in the grass among those fourteen- through seventeen-year-olds that day feeling a sense of pride, calm, accomplishment, and strength that I had never experienced. Ever. I was hooked.

We moved, I started teaching at a different school, Bret started getting paid more, and I stopped coaching. But I kept running. Mile after mile, faster and faster. I had a baby and added a jogging stroller to my entourage. I could be found sailing through the streets ten miles at a time with a baby and dog for company. Once my daughter decided this whole thing was boring, I started increasing my speed, and seven-minute miles were a regular thing. My dog was FAST!

In the meantime, over in my professional life, I wrote a book about teaching writing in high school and used running and writing as the opening metaphor. It resonated with runners and writers alike. Six books later, it's still the piece people come to me to talk about. However, right after that first book was published, I suffered an injury, and at thirty years old, I was facing hip surgery or ending my running career.

Enter yoga. I was writing another book, this time with colleagues, and I couldn't sit in a chair because my hip hurt so badly. Shana, one of my coauthors, (this was when we met, all those many years ago) was likewise suffering, and the two of us worked on our bellies on the university office floor. She suggested I try yoga as it was helping her. I was *really* skeptical, but she had been a college athlete, and was a general badass, so I gave it a try. It was me and Shiva Rae's DVD in the living room, learning what *vinyasa* flow yoga was all about. (It means "to place in a special way" in Sanskrit, in other words, moving with intention.) And *then* a hot yoga studio opened up a mile from my house.

For nearly twenty years now, I have replaced my seven-minute miles with hot, banging, vinyasa yoga. It's athletic, it's challenging, and it shakes out the collywobbles in the same way my pounding runs did. If I were writing this book three years ago, it would have been a rewrite about *yoga* and writing. I would have been drawing similar connections to writing that I did in the first piece. The daunting task of starting. The first, hard five minutes, and then the feeling of flying when I'd nail a warrior III with my arms interlaced behind my back and every muscle firing all at the same time, balanced in a laser focus that felt like I could hold it *all day long.* I would have said this is what happens in mid-flow with my writing. I am strong, I am balanced, I am flying, and I have the stamina to go all day. And while all of that's true, it still would have been a book about writing, which this is not.

What changed? I decided to become a *yoga* teacher in addition to my writing teacher career. During the 500-hour process of becoming certified, I learned that there is a lot more to yoga than the poses or *asana*. In fact, the Yoga Sutras say there are eight limbs, and asana is number three! I was just scratching the surface with my practice. The first limb points to practicing non-harming or non-violence in thought, word, and deed. For me, it was about practicing grace, for myself and for others. I started wondering, what if I approached yoga, writing, and *life* in this way? And suddenly, a career of writing that had me churning out words for predetermined publications six to seven days a week started to look like a daily habit of writing just for myself, exploring who I was and where I'd been, with no thought of publication.

You see, while the writing I had been doing before was serving me professionally, it was not feeding my soul. I was harming myself. There was no peace. Just like with the running and even the constant need for hot, banging asana as my daily practice, I was constantly struggling with injuries or beating myself up for missing a practice when priorities took precedence, or I was simply exhausted. I felt, deep in my bones, that the only way I could calm my mind was to push my body to its absolute limit on a daily basis. I was mistaken.

Sure, I was writing books that were being published and getting a lot of positive professional feedback that made me feel good about myself as an academic and a "productive" human, but I wasn't writing what I truly wanted to explore, which was non-academic work, a memoir, some fiction. I wasn't showing up for myself in my writing. I did the work, got the accolades, but it wasn't *magic*. And I was sacrificing a lot in my life to write for the academy rather than in ways that truly mattered to me. It was an injury to my soul.

All of those things I did, from step aerobics, to running, to churning out academic writing weren't wrong. They were a part of my journey. They were my practice. But they were not my peace. I tell myself to notice rather than judge them.

So that's the short story of how I got to where I am at this moment. Teaching yoga, coaching writers, studying and practicing the deeper aspects of yoga in addition to my beloved banging asana, and learning how to calm my mind without punishing my body.

In short, my work is about what happened when one woman stopped running and started to practice stillness. You know, that pause I began the book with that my grandma was teaching me at her knee? I spent my early adulthood running *flat out*. On the road, then with my yoga practice when the road became physically impossible, but also in my parenting, my work, and my academic life, even in my partnership with my husband. At the peak of my running, I was working on a PhD, working a full-time job at the university, and raising two small children while helping my husband care for his aging grandparents. Each morning began before 5 a.m., as if I had been shot from a cannon, and my days carried on that way until well after 11 p.m. I was praised by everyone for my productivity. My husband thought I could do and handle anything. I thought *I* was a badass.

But running flat out in life is unsustainable. Life is a marathon, and I was running a 100-meter dash pace all.of.the.time. I was out of control, and I could feel it, which only made me run harder and faster away from the fear this loss of control was creating. I became grumpy, then belligerent, then filled with rage at the slightest provocation.

In the film *The Princess Bride,* the Fire Swamp serves as a metaphor for trouble. In the Fire Swamp, the characters avoid getting singed once they learn that there is a "strange popping sound" before flames burst out of the earth. The rage was "that strange popping sound" for my husband and me. After having to bash out the same dangerous conflagrations more than a few times, we realized that something was very, very wrong.

That's when the real work began. I started to remember and relearn the tools to slow down and relish life, even, and especially, when it is hard or scary, rather than running from it. I started to dig deep and cultivate my tender roots that yearned for the pause, rest, and, yes, savasana.

WHEN THE WORK
IS MAGIC

These days, my "job" is as a yoga instructor and writing coach. I'm also a writer. And none of it "feels" like work. The hustle and grind just isn't a real part of it. Sometimes I make up scenarios that make me feel like hustle and grind are there and needed, but that is self-imposed, and my *actual* work is to keep that self-inflicted trauma at bay.

It was a cold, rainy January day. I had a cold. I felt crappy.

It was also a writing workshop day for the group of authors with whom I work. My job was to show up, respond, and write. I had my own book to write. I had another collaborative project I was working on. I was low, low energy.

I began my morning with a meditation about learning to honor our seasons and cycles (aka how to stop bulldozing oneself) and went back to bed.

I did manage a shower, but doing my hair for the Zoom call was not in the cards. I knew I didn't have to show up at all. And I knew I needed to see faces, to be in community. And I knew these women couldn't care less about the way I looked.

So there I was in the writing workshop. I showed up for myself and only for myself. I needed people. I needed to write. I needed the people in order to write.

And then … magic. There was a huge holding of space for one another. The details didn't matter. What mattered was that each of these women showed up for themselves on a craptastic day, and in so doing, showed up for each other. No one had the answers. Everyone was imperfect. We were just there, holding one another up.

And it was more than enough.

It was Sunday afternoon at 4:15 p.m. I was exhausted. I sat in front of the fire with my head in my hands thinking about canceling the 5 p.m. yoga class that was to happen on Zoom. My phone buzzed. A Venmo from JPG, a long time friend, for the class. That meant at least one person was counting on me. I started to talk to myself: "You know teaching yoga lights you up. And you know JPG is ready for this. Just do it. Just show up."

Through sheer force of will, I set up the computer and found the music I needed to hear. JPG popped on, and as we were getting started, two more beautiful souls joined in, one of which was a new student but a dear old friend, Lacy. Seeing their faces pop on the screen energized me. Immediately. We did the warm-up and hit the standing sequence, and the whole practice shifted into gear. These women who had made space for themselves pinged an inspirational key in my heart strings. And then, as Lauren Daigle crooned "Look Up Child" on the playlist, Lacy hit updog, shoulders spread, heart shining, eyes on the sky, and a look of utter joy and peace on her face. I had chills.

We finished the standing sequence, and I cued a five-minute pigeon pose. JPG applauded. These yogis were on fire with what they were doing for themselves on this day.

But, as it would happen, with twenty minutes left in this amazing practice, the Internet went out, and I lost Zoom. I scrambled back on, and there was JPG, leading the rest through what she thought I might do next. We finished the practice with no music, only the sounds of our breathing and my voice with my camera turned off, lest the Internet poltergeist strike again. We even agreed that the universe was calling for a silent savasana.

I signed off, completely and utterly inspired, energized, and uplifted. I shot a quick email apologizing for the tech difficulties and thanking the yogis for their practice. And I thought I had hit my peak for the night, remembering why I teach yoga. But the universe wasn't done with me.

Lacy wrote back, thanking me. She let me know that she had abandoned her practice, which had been a solid one, since her father died, but her body had been craving what we were doing that afternoon. I cannot describe the deep honor I felt in being a part of helping an amazing woman, whom I so admire, find her way back to her mat. Magic.

It was Thursday evening. I showed up to the studio on one of those beautiful, break-in-the-weather days we get in February in North Carolina. The temperatures had topped out over 70 that day, and it was a glorious night, which translates as "hard to go inside." Needless to say, I was expecting a small crowd. I opened the windows to let out the steam and let in the glorious night air as soon as I got in the studio, and then shut them again, because it *is* a hot class. As the yogis trickled in, I was astounded. It was packed. And to my surprise, a former captain in the US Army and five young men from a local college baseball team walked in. They had all done "a little" yoga but were very new to the practice. None of them were "typical" yogis.

Yet they hung with me, listening carefully to cues, looking around to see what I meant by the postures I was calling, comfortable with my touch in assists, at peace with their tightness as well as my words about finding space on and off the mat. At one point, I cued a modified side angle, and thirty yogis of all shapes, sizes, and abilities became one, with perfect, graceful lines from ankle to wrist. Chills again. I gave the pose a few extra breaths as the unity swept over the room.

As for the captain and the baseball boys, they were all squarely on their mats, doing their work, and not at all concerned about the new place in which they'd found themselves. And they all stayed for savasana, which is often the hardest pose for active people, lying on the floor in stillness for five full minutes. Afterward, they were all smiles, promising to return, glowing with what they had found on their mats. They showed up.

As I lead yoga practices and writing workshops, people often find themselves in long, intense poses and long periods of writing space. Pigeon pose is a great example. One leg is positioned at a right angle at the top of the mat, the other stretched out behind, flat, hip points aimed down into the mat; yogis are often lying with their faces *on* the mat or on a block and arms stretched overhead. It's an intense posture (and has a great modification on the back for those who aren't wanting to go that deep in that moment). A great example of this intensity is the thirty-minute writing sprint. Butt glued to the chair and fingers on keys or pen moving across the page making words come what may. In both situations, I find myself coaching, "Go to *your* edge. Explore that edge. Where can you find ease? Where can you let go? Where can you find space?"

The magic is in each of *our* edges. Not someone else's. Ease and space. The letting go. These are the things I want to find not just on mats and on paper, but in life.

So I tell myself, and others, yes! Commit to the habit (the practice), but listen to your body and your mind for what you need this day. There should be no pain, but there can be deep, challenging sensation, or even discomfort. Discomfort is okay. It can be growth. Pain is injury. Stay on your own mat or page (path). Don't get so caught up in producing for an audience or being as "bendy" or as "strong" as the person next to you. And don't feel like every day needs to be banging asana or 600 flawless words. Practice in community and in nature. Draw energy and give energy to those around you. Neither yoga nor writing is practiced in a vacuum, and neither is life. We have the sutras and teachings of others to guide our practice. But ultimately, it's our own practice. For us. Not for those who are watching.

And that is where the work can become the evolution at the roots. The magic!

Part 3

EVOLVING. SLOWLY.

REST, AMAZON WOMAN

I lay in at least a foot of snow, my then sixteen-year-old daughter buried underneath me, my left leg shooting pain and tangled in a tree, the gasoline smell of the snowmobile's motor choking me as it rumbled nearby. "Are you okay?" I managed to keep the fear out of my voice. My daughter giggled. She giggled! "Sure, I'm fine, just buried in the snow and can't move because you are on top of me." She was okay. It was only me that was hurt, and it was only my leg. That, we could work with. "Now what?" was my next and only thought. On that snow trail in the middle of nowhere, I was totally calm and business-like. We had to get out of the snow. I had to get to some help. There were jobs to do.

Some years earlier, I'd found myself sprawled face first in the street, my left pinky finger wrapped around my hand at a very unnatural angle after losing control of the three Great Danes and a pit bull mix I was walking to the bus stop. I stood up, called my husband, rounded up the dogs while waving off the neighbor who came running out to help me, and walked to the bus stop to meet my kids, bloody knees and all. The dogs needed to be safe, my kids needed to be met at the bus stop, and then I needed to get some help. There was business to attend to.

Some years before *that*, I was pelting along running, listening to "Wake Me Up Inside," when my feet got tangled up with the dog, and I hit the ground, square on my left hip, hard. I picked myself up and ran another six miles before limping home. I popped some Advil and moved on, to the extreme detriment of my hip, which would eventually end my running career.

The Amazon woman persona sounds (in my own head) like an attribute; calm in the midst of chaos and all of that. What I'm coming to learn is that the Amazon woman persona is actually a symptom of what gets me into these chaotic situations in the first place. I am *not* an Amazon woman. But there are times when I am moving way too fast, and I think I can take on the world. I think I can walk three Great Danes and a pit bull. I think I can wrangle a snowmobile with zero visibility. I think I can run ten miles. And it's not that I *can't* do those things and haven't successfully before; it's that doing those things while feeling all-powerful and invincible, while being in a state of delusion, is a bad, bad idea. The truth is that when I feel invincible, I am at my most vulnerable.

Some days I have the energy of an Amazon woman. I feel GREAT! I'm ready to take on the world. I not only feel like I can handle all of the jobs of a working wife and mother, but also like I can take on systemic issues in public schools and perhaps even end systemic poverty and racism. I plan lots of things. I say yes to all the projects. I execute on everything. I am a machine. Remember the bulldozer? I'm a machine that chews up and spits out anything that gets in her way, including, and especially, her family. And there's the rub. The all-powerful Amazon-woman feeling quickly turns to rage because people aren't moving fast enough and are In. My. Way. What is needed is the courage to find balance.

Let me back up. The entire story of the snowmobile debacle needs telling. You may have gathered by now that I am an active sort, as is my family. In December 2017, we decided to gather up my mother-in-law and head to the Adirondacks for Christmas break. The resort was a ranch of sorts that offered snow skiing, tubing, horseback riding, sleigh riding, and snowmobiling all day every day as a part of the all-inclusive rate. We gloried in the -12-degree weather and took full advantage of all that was offered for the week.

On the last day of the trip, I was ramping up. We had one day left, and I felt the glory of the vacation was fleeting. All day long, my husband reminded me to be careful and slow down, to find balance. But I wanted to do *all* the things and be *all* the fun for my kids. I didn't have the courage to find stillness and seek the balance my husband was begging me to search for. I was wrapped up in the old narrative of discipline: to be and do all the things, to get our money's worth out of the "all inclusive" package, to not miss an opportunity to *do* something to make a memory with my teenage children, to keep going, to keep pushing, to keep moving.

Around 3 p.m., my husband pulled me aside before hitting the slope with the kids and said, "You are really racing. *Please* take some time now to *slow down*." It wasn't really that I didn't listen to him; it's that I *couldn't* do it. I felt *awesome*, like I could take on the world. Having not yet fully realized these moments as the strange popping sounds of the Fire Swamp, and not really heeding my husband's dire warning and concern, I decided it would be a great idea to take my daughter on one last snowmobile ride before the place shut everything down.

We rushed out to meet the last snowmobile group for the day, grabbed helmets, and jammed them over our winter hats. Mine didn't fit properly, and I was having a little trouble seeing, but in my all-powerful state, I figured it would be okay. And off I went driving a snowmobile with my sixteen-year-old daughter on the back, through the woods, with an ill-fitting helmet, not quite able to see.

Things went fine at first, although I was craning my neck to see through the visor. I kept telling myself that all I had to do was follow the snowmobile in front of me, and all would be well. It was a big target, so it should be fine. And I had no fear. So there was that. I was taking my daughter on one last ride. I was the cool mom who could do anything. All was glorious.

And then we hit a wicked turn. I say "wicked" because that's what the cowboy said later. The one who dug us out of the snow. When we hit the turn, the right ski on my snowmobile hit a snowdrift, because I did not turn at the correct angle, because I didn't see it coming. The handle bars jerked out of my hands, and we went off trail, hurtling toward a very large tree. "Oh God," my brain rambled, "this is going to hurt! And we've just paid for our daughter to play travel volleyball!"

I managed to get the steering back in hand just in time to slam the break and veer around the tree with the machine, but my left tibia hit said tree with full impact, and we were both thrown from the snow mobile.

Lying there in the snowdrift, I did know that I was hurt, but that was not top of mind. "Are you okay?" I said, manifesting as much of a "yes" answer as I have ever tried to muster. To my complete relief, Mackenzie was fine. The relief I felt was unsurpassed. I pause here to say this could have been so very much worse.

I told Mackenzie that I was not okay and to be still as all the people who had been on the trail with us descended on the crash scene. We were buried in the snow and tangled in the tree. They dug us out, hacked through the tree, and somehow got me up on one foot, but I couldn't even begin to hop back to the trail. We all stood there for a moment in the freezing cold trying to figure out what to do when a kind, young cowboy said, "I'm going to make this easy," and scooped me up. He carried me to his snowmobile and asked if I could drive. When I assured him that there was no way, he calmly said, "No problem; hang on," and jumped in the driver's seat. "My daughter can't drive either!" I shouted above the rumble of the motor. "Don't worry ma'am; we've got her," he shouted back before taking off like a scalded cat.

I can only describe the drive back to the lodge as terrifying. This guy was experienced on those trails and on a snowmobile and very intent on getting me back to the lodge ASAP. I just buried my head in the stranger's back, wrapped my arms around him, and prayed to the universe and all that may have had any power over my arriving back at the lodge alive.

We made it back, and the kind young cowboy carried me to a chair, and the lodge staff came running with blankets and hot sweet tea. As they got me settled in, my girl came running in asking again if I was okay. "No," I said, "and you are going to have to go to the slopes and find your father because his cell is right here in my pocket." She scooted back out the door, *actually* calm and cool in a crisis. I couldn't have been prouder.

It wasn't long before my husband showed up, and he looked thunderous. Thunderous is his terrified face. By this time, I was going into shock and was unable to answer the questions he was firing at me. I looked to my daughter, who was sitting quietly in the corner, and said, "Can you please answer your father's questions?" They went back and forth for a bit trying to determine how it was that I had driven us into a tree, and then he left to get the car and our son so we could get me to urgent care.

Why, you may ask, didn't we call an ambulance? Several reasons: (1) It never occurred to us. I don't think either of us thought the injury was as bad as it was. (2) We were in the middle of nowhere. (3) Ambulances are expensive.

After a horrendous ride in the back seat over miles of icy roads and a stop at the "wrong" urgent care, we finally made it to a place that could help us. The receptionist took one look at me, and they whipped me back and started covering me with warm blankets. I was shaking from head to toe even though I'd been out of the snow and had the heat blasting for over an hour. Shock. For real.

And in my shock, all I could think was, "I have really hairy legs, and I'm not wearing any drawers under all these layers of spandex." In defiance of said shock, I actually texted this information to my daughter and mother-in-law who were waiting back at the lodge, just so they'd know I was going to be okay. Because taking care of my people was where my mind was. I was an Amazon woman after all!

The X-ray, however, told a different story. I had an eight-inch fracture, and the urgent care doctor was worried about how close it was to my knee. No messing around, I was going by ambulance to the nearest hospital, over twenty miles away over more icy roads in the dark, for surgery that night. I was stunned. I got focused inward in a hurry.

As it turned out, once I made it to the hospital, the orthopedist there decided that my knee was not in danger (thank you, bendy ligaments brought to me by yoga) and surgery could wait. So I was released with a lot of pain meds and a giant soft brace that went from ankle to groin. Back in the car I went, on the icy roads back to the lodge where my husband carried me up icy steps and into our chalet. After a sleepless night, there was the fifteen-hour drive back to North Carolina in the back of a packed Subaru with my leg on my thirteen year-old son's lap while he desperately tried not to move. It was as much fun as you are imagining.

As it was New Years Eve when we drove home, I didn't actually see a doctor until two days later, and it was a full week before I had surgery to repair what I'd done to myself. The result was a nine-inch plate with eight screws.

It takes six months to recover from such an injury, three of which are spent on crutches, not putting any weight on the broken leg. And then a second bout of crutches when the hardware was removed because my body couldn't stand having it in there. Without the outlets of yoga and long walks, I was ready to lose my ever-loving mind. My anger at myself and the fact that I was over being stuck on the couch exacerbated that situation. It took hours and hours of work on affirmations, many long talks with the husband, and a *lot* of therapy to pull me back from the edge of insanity. I was a ball of rage.

My therapist insisted that I needed to find some sort of release valve for all the anger. For years, I had told students that poetry was an outlet for strong emotions, so I decided to take myself at my own word. The result was a poem making heavy use of the f-bomb and then a second part reminding me to turn inward and find my Zen.

Writing the poem was cathartic and healing. Reading it over and over became a daily regimen as it took me through the extreme emotions to a space of acceptance that I had to start again with every day. Because every day, I woke up angry as all get out, and full of bitter thoughts toward myself for having landed in such a predicament. The poem helped me release it all safely and find some grace and stillness.

In my months of recovery, when sitting with my therapist, talking with my husband, and in quiet moments when I'd been trying to pull myself together, I recognized that there was much to learn from this whole experience. First, I was so lucky. It was just a leg, and legs heal. There was no permanent damage, and my daughter was unscathed. Second, and of the utmost importance, when I feel like an Amazon woman, I need to have the courage to take a step back and park myself until the feeling passes. And when my husband recognizes it before I do, I need to dig deep, get over myself, and take a *giant* step back, and park myself until the feeling passes. Not doing that put my family and myself through months of needless torment. I have gotten that particular lesson through my thick head now. Before the epic leg disaster, a part of me gloried in the Amazon woman feeling. It's an awesome feeling. I feel unstoppable and invincible and like I can take on anything and everything. But it's not real, and it is very, very dangerous.

I also learned for the first time in my forty-four years how to slow and calm myself without pounding my body into the ground. I learned how to make space and find stillness. Early on, it was running. Later, I found hot, sweaty yoga. There is nothing wrong with these things, and I returned to yoga as soon as the doctors cleared me, but I learned that I don't have to wait until I can get to a class. I can sit in silence and breathe. I can meditate. I can control and calm my racing mind. There is a gift in every problem, and the ability to slow down was the gift of six months on the sofa. Turns out, all of those months of sitting with myself is exactly what I needed to practice pausing. And it gave me power over my mind in a way I had never imagined.

Now, it wouldn't have taken me all of these years to figure out that my Amazon woman persona didn't serve me if I had been *honest* with myself way back when I had to give up running. The same is true for the incident with the dogs and the badly broken finger. I did seek medical attention for my disasters, but I did not have the *courage* to be honest about what was really happening in my head. That, I hid. To my own detriment and that of my family. But the universe got my attention with the whole snowmobile-and-tree experience.

I'd love to say that I completely stopped all of the running after the snowmobile incident, but as I keep saying, life is practice. What the snowmobile taught me is that I am not invincible. It also brought home the message of Bret's Grandpa who always told us, "When you are in a hurry, slow down." Talk about some sage advice.

I am capable and powerful, yes, but not an Amazon woman. I can do all the things, but not in a big hurry. When I feel that push, I need to *slow down*, reach and tend those roots of the pause. I need to come back to my body. And only then can I proceed, because while running flat out is great for a short, *intentional* sprint, it will crush a girl to take the marathon of life at that pace. The path, I am finding, is to have the courage to find balance.

MY BODY WILL
LET ME KNOW

I was halfway through a hot yoga class, breathing, moving and sweating happily, feeling powerful in my own body and thrilled with myself for making it to a 6 a.m. practice in the dark and cold of January.

I extended into a fully balanced, beautiful, dancer posture, and a searing pain shot through my chest and down my right arm.

"Dammit!" I thought. "I've pulled something in my chest!"

And I kept practicing, attempting to loosen it up.

But the pain only gripped more tightly, and then I couldn't breathe. By sheer force of will yet again, I picked up my mat and drug it out of the studio, stumbling and bumping into startled yogis, and made it to the locker room where I sank to the floor, back against the wall, and put my head between my knees, just as everything started to go black.

I sat there panting and reviewing my options.

Alerting my teacher was a solid "no." The whole studio would empty out to help. Plus, there was no getting off the floor.

I could crawl to my phone and call the front desk, but the girl working there was about twelve years old and would surely freak out.

I could call Bret, but he was still asleep and most likely wouldn't hear the phone, and *would* most likely have a heart attack himself.

So I sat and worked to calm my breathing. Eventually the pain ebbed a bit, and the tunnel vision opened up. I could get air into my lungs. So I got up and drove the 1.5 miles home.

On the drive, I had a talk with myself about the seriousness of the situation. I mean, there was that whole *Grey's Anatomy* season where Bailey had a heart attack and no one would believe her because they are so hard to find in women. I convinced myself that something needed to be done and pretty quickly, but I was *drenched* in sweat from yoga. Like soaking wet. So a quick shower was my first order of business. That done, I gently woke Bret and described my symptoms, and as expected, he flew into action, getting me settled in my chair, and getting our doctor on the phone.

No, we didn't just go to the hospital. That just wasn't our way. Yet. Thank goodness we have a wonderful, trusted primary care doc who tells us when we are being pig headed. This time, I didn't even get past the nurse. She listened, asked some questions, and sent me to urgent care.

Things got crazy from there. Urgent care is connected to the ER. They looked at me, listened to my story, and said, "Do you want to walk next door, or do we need to get transport?"

I walked. Because, well, I didn't want to pay for transport if it was just next door.

Now, I was fussy about going to the ER in the first place because they have a reputation for LOOONNGG waits. Let me tell you what. Walk in with heart attack symptoms, and there is no waiting. Lickety split, they got me all tucked in and hooked up to monitors. Word got out that I had been at yoga when all this went down and was, in fact, a yoga teacher. With a heart rate of 49 and blood pressure hanging around 90 over whatever to boot. After doing all the enzyme tests that they do, the lovely doctor came in and said, "You are a badass, and it doesn't look like you are having a heart attack, but we are going to keep you and dig deeper just to be sure."

I stayed, they repeated the enzyme test after the appropriate amount of time while my symptoms came and went, and they found nothing, not even COVID. So I went home to rest. That was a Friday.

My symptoms continued throughout the night and into the morning. Again, I couldn't decide about going back to the hospital. Finally, a friend called said trusted doctor, who called *me* and asked what the hell I was doing and, in no uncertain words, sent me back to the hospital. More tests, and I got to stay overnight. Still nothing. I came home.

My symptoms persisted, and I couldn't get out of a chair without blacking out. I called my doctor with an update on Monday, and he said, "I'm afraid you have to go back to the hospital." This time, a heart catheterization was ordered. The good news is that they have a machine that does imaging for that if you can be VERY still and hold your breath, so no actual surgery was required. It was clear. Nothing there. The cardiologist said I had the heart of a really healthy twenty-eight-year-old. Yet I still couldn't get out of my chair.

Over the next two months there were many tests and specialists looking for some pretty scary things. I was exhausted all of the time and still couldn't stand up without blacking out. Yet all of the tests came back clean and beautiful. I was the picture of health.

Except that I wasn't.

After scouring the Internet and doing a ton of research, my husband suggested that I get my hormone levels checked. My doctor sent me straight down the hall to have it done. The results were baffling. It seems I had gone totally and completely through menopause without even noticing. I had no estrogen in my body. My doctor gave me an estrogen patch, and within twenty-four hours, I felt like I could take on the world.

Now, *how,* you might ask, does a woman go *totally* through menopause without knowing it? It's a fair question. In my defense, I'd had a hysterectomy years before, so no obvious signs there. But the real answer is that I simply wasn't paying attention to my body. When the doctor asked if I'd ever had night sweats, I said, "No." My husband gently said, "What about when you throw off all of the covers and your clothes in the middle of the night like they are on fire?" Um, yep. That had happened quite a bit and more frequently over the past year. I had also been a good bit more fatigued, but I had just chalked that up to the stress of living through a global pandemic during which:

- My husband was in the process of selling his business and was working from home, having stressful conversations with clients, letting them know what was happening.
- My college-attending daughter had to come home and was having big feelings about that.
- My son was doing high school from home.
- I was teaching college English online from home.

You know, just a few plates spinning.

I wasn't having a heart attack in yoga. It was a panic attack. Now, I know that a symptom of menopause can be serious heart palpitations and panic attacks. Those can also be brought on by crazy stress. It was a double whammy.

I thought I was "handling my stress" because I was practicing yoga every day. *Every* day, from November 1 to December 31. Sixty-two days straight. Hot, banging asana. But that was *all* that I was doing for myself. There was no looking inward. There was no stillness, no pause. I was pouring every ounce of energy into the people around me and their needs, but I was not tending to my own except for that one hour a day on my mat. And I often had one, if not both, of my kids with me when that was happening. There is absolutely nothing wrong with bringing one's babies to yoga. In fact, I encourage it. Some of my favorite practices have been those shared with my children. We are doing it together, offering our energy to one another. It's a beautiful thing. But I was unable to detach and look inward. And I missed all of the signs that my body was changing and that it was depleted. Until the universe hit me with a sack of hammers.

At first, I was horribly embarrassed. I mean, who has a panic attack in *yoga* of all places? Who, when feeling great about showing up, about her strength and power and flexibility, who, in *that* moment, has a full-on panic attack?

Well, I'll tell you who. A person who is not looking inward, who is not paying attention, who is not slowing down and showing up for herself. In the midst of all of the madness, there is one more thing I haven't told you about. I was auditioning to teach at the yoga studio that I called home. It was going poorly. It felt like middle school cheerleading tryouts, where I was horrible and wanted it so badly that I couldn't see straight. Due to lack of estrogen, I couldn't memorize a sequence to save my life—and memorization was 100 percent required—while also dealing with the mic and the music and the lights and the humidity and assisting. Post estrogen patch, I can do it all with ease, like a dance. But at that time, I was a complete wreck. I worked and worked. I drilled and drilled. I couldn't do it. And let me tell you, other than middle school cheerleading, that was a new experience.

I didn't get the job. The studio owner gently told me to keep teaching online, get some more hours under my belt, and come back in a few months. I was crushed, heartbroken, and mortified. See, I even saved it for later in the chapter because there is still a small part of me that doesn't want to admit that the failure affected me so drastically.

At the time, I told myself that my family was more important than teaching yoga, and they were all in huge need. I told myself that this failure, because let's face it, that's how I saw it, was the universe telling me to pay attention to my people. So I squashed down all the desire and shame and sadness and soldiered on. I used up even more of my energy for others. Until my body and the universe put me in the chair.

Sounding familiar? Perhaps you are saying, "Cindy, for all of your lessons with the broken leg, you seem to have missed something." You would be right. I missed showing up for myself by not taking a moment. Taking a deep breath. Sitting in stillness even when not forced to by an injury. How many times have I said to a friend with deep, honest love and compassion, "You have to put your oxygen mask on first." Yet I did not take my own advice.

I am still learning these lessons. Just four years after breaking my leg, I injured my back. I forgot for a moment that I was forty-seven years old rather than twenty-two and did one too many handstands when the arthritis in my hips was acting up due to cold weather, and I was tired. My back let me know. So I did the things, did the PT, learned that my deep stabilizers could use some work, and that, dammit, if I was going to get upside down, I'd need to do some planking. All good.

Then I took my "healed" back on a six-hour drive to Amelia Island, Florida, for a writing retreat. In my head, this was my week to "get my wind back" before hitting the hot studio. My plan was to walk the beach each morning before breakfast, teach yoga, and then practice around noon for a half hour, half of what I would normally do. It was a solid, reasonable plan.

On the first morning, I woke up to a mind-blowing sunrise, 33-degree temps, and feeling stiff as a board. My body was reminding me of the drive I had so effortlessly taken the day before. Even six months prior, I would have bundled up and headed out to the beach for that walk because, you know, "discipline" equals freedom. But instead, that morning, I tuned in and listened to my body. I showed up, inside of the sliding glass door on my yoga mat, slowly and carefully stretching out the stiffness. No walk. And with deep, deep satisfaction and pride about that decision. The walk would have been the antithesis of discipline. It would have been irresponsible. I still received the magic of the sunrise over the water, but in a way that honored my body and all she can do for me. I listened. And the reward was an opening up. A letting go of tightness. A finding of space. A place of pure joy and magic. Grace.

Will I be able to hold on forever to this practice of radical acceptance for myself and what I need, of turning inward and listening? Doubtful. Because I am not perfect, nor will I ever be. But I don't have to be. I get to learn and grow. I get to get better at listening and learning. I get to show up and practice. I get to evolve.

AFFIRMING EVOLUTION

Finally, after living through all the broken things and panic attacks, I sat down and created the affirmation below. For a long time, I read it each morning. It was written in my journals, transferring from one to the next as I ran out of pages, and beautifully decorated. I don't turn to it daily anymore because it has become a part of me, and I can reach for it when I need it. When times are dark, I find the last place I wrote it and let the words wash over me.

> *I am a joyful breeze entering a room. I accept my power. I go beyond barriers to possibilities. I choose to let go and trust in order to take real control of my life. I commit to letting go of destructive fears and doubts and of anger and bitterness. I commit to feel good about myself each day. Every morning I commit to remind myself that I can make the choice to feel good. I commit to*

cultivating this habit. I commit to patience
and tolerance with and of others and
myself. In this way, I control my reactions to
my surroundings.

These words, the ones that I crafted, leaning on other affirmation models, calm my spirit and remind me of who I am. Just now, as I reread them to begin drafting my concluding thoughts to the book, I felt my spirits lift and soar. When I do the work of reaching for affirmations that *I* wrote, that *I* believe, that *I* trust, I feel better, lighter, freer.

Along with this affirmation, I have something called a *jiva* code (or soul code). When I was doing my 200-hour yoga training, we were asked to create a sentence or phrase that encompassed who we were and who we wanted to be. It was to be the code we lived by, our unique purpose on the planet. I wrote pages and pages to come up with the following.

I am fearlessly accepting, wildly authentic,
persistently truthful, relentlessly kind.

After working for a week to get these words just right, I have carried them with me since that time. They encompass the woman I endeavor to be on any given day. I don't always hit the mark because

I am human, but the words mark what I am always reaching for. So much so that they are my description on social media. I have used them in my biography for the website of the writing coach business I'm a part of and for my yoga instructor profile. These words remind me of who I am, at the root, and who I am evolving to become.

Life is not easy. Doing "the work" of nurturing one's roots is hard. But when we do that work, the leaves bud and flourish, and we continue to grow and evolve.

Epilogue

EVOLVING FROM THE ROOTS

y grandparents were deeply in love, and affectionately so, for fifty years. My parents are besotted with one another and in their fifty-fourth year of marriage. Love and passion over time is the story I was raised on. It's also the story I'm living.

Yet …

I wrote the following as a possible social media post long after the book you are reading was "completed" and sent to my editor.

> *My web designer (who happens to be a dear friend and straight shooter) was offering feedback on my "About Me" page. She read it as "I'm a Mom" and then some other stuff. I felt a cultural pull to "fix" it and was angry about it all at the same time.*

Brené Brown tells us that anger is the tip of the emotional iceberg, so I peeked below the surface and found profound sadness there for a world in which Mom is not the thing that tops the resume. And I recognize that this is not mine to "fix." It's a part of the world I get to be with.

To research ...
To breathe through ...
To write about ...

Cindy Urbanski, PhD in Urban Literacy
Cindy Urbanski, RYT 500 Yoga Instructor
Ethnographer
Published Author
Teacher
Coach

These are my "professional" titles. There was a time in my life where I thought they defined me. But they never quite fit. They were sort of like an itchy sweater or pants that are just a little too tight.

The "title" that has always felt right, comfortable, perfect, like my favorite worn-in jeans, is Mom. My partner of 30 years and I have had the privilege of parenting two children. And now, as they are bursting into adulthood and my daughter has found her person, I have three! I am so excited for what's next for all of my children.

"MOM" be it a text rendered in all caps, a phone call, or hollered through the house, snaps me back to the moment, the present, the now. It's in my mothering that I am most grounded.

Yeah,
I am a PhD
I am a published author of academia and
 edgy literary nonfiction
I am a researcher and ethnographer
I am a writing coach
I am a 500 hour certified yoga instructor

And first,
I AM Mom!

In and amongst all those titles and the accolades they bring, I have the distinct honor of holding space, being with and parenting these amazing humans. Each day I get to bear witness to their greatness and all they bring to the world.

So, yes, in my "About Me" section of my website, I make mention of my children and my role as Mom. That's not a widely popular stance. Some may even call it irresponsible. I call it rocking a boat that sorely needs rocking.

I fired the draft off to Bret, my most honest and trusted reader, certain down to my bones that he would love it. I was claiming my motherhood as the most important thing and positioning it in a way I would not have had the guts to claim ten years ago. I expected pride and accolades about how far I've come.

As it turns out, he told me the truth, as he can always be counted on to do. He noted that I had left out my role as "wife," except for a small, timid aside. Not because I don't value our twenty-eight years of marriage and thirty-year relationship and partnership, but because like "mom" on the resume, "wife" falls even deeper into the "not listed" well.

And here's the evolution that is still occurring.

The bulldozer engines revived, and I immediately went back and "added" in my role as wife as blatantly and plainly and proudly as I had my mothering because he is right in that it is a role I value in my deepest parts. I fired that draft back at my husband with a "THANK YOU" and was met with silence. Here's the evolving. I recognized Bret's silence as space to think.

I shut down the engines.

I reached for my tool box.

I pondered, slowly and deeply.

I did not panic.

I halted the internal conversations about what a horrible wife I am.

I thought on why I had been so timid about our tremendous life together.

For weeks.

And then I finished reading Ariel Lawhon's *The Frozen River*. I flipped to the back flap. The last sentence of Lawhon's biography caught my eye and landed on my heart. "Lawhon splits her time between the grocery store and the baseball field."

Lawhon is a best-selling author. The book I had just finished devouring was a well-researched, artfully crafted piece of historical fiction about the power of women and the ancient art of midwifery, yes, and *also* the power of long, deep marriage and true partnership. The author's note hit me right where I'm still evolving. Right at the root.

Even as my book is done and finished, back from the editor and ready for production, I am evolving. My roots are sinking deeper into the earth, and I am pausing and lingering rather than reacting. I wrote the initial social media post to *investigate* anger rather than respond *out* of anger. I didn't panic at my sweet husband's comments, but took them in and considered the deep, trusted truth of them. I got grounded and pondered them as these words flowed from my fingers onto the screen. Imperfect questions, not answers. Tools in the toolbox that I've been filling all this time. Tools that ground a person in the cultivation of self and connect her to the work. Tools, plural, rather than a singular bulldozer.

And that's what I want to leave you with. Tending the roots by hand and doing the work does not give us all of the answers. What happens when we do the work to cultivate our roots and evolve is we develop a pretty hefty toolbox. And if we are open to it, those around us add to that toolbox.

The collecting of tools is the evolution. It is ongoing and day-to-day. When we are rooted, and open, those tools come to us, like magic. Except it's not. It's the work.

ACKNOWLEDGMENTS

There is a practice with which I end each yoga class I have the privilege of leading. I invite everyone to a seated position with eyes cast down or closed, and then ask that we all bring our hands to heart center in prayer. These are the words I speak into the room and the universe. These are the words that touch my soul.

> *In deep gratitude to yourself, for showing up on your mat today to feed your mind, your body, and your spirit. In deep gratitude for those who have practiced with you and offered up their powerful, beautiful energy. And in deep gratitude for those that have made this time possible for you today.*

This prayer of gratitude is what came to mind as I was scribbling in my journal about what in the world I wanted to put in the acknowledgments of this book.

There was a powerful healing in the writing and revising of these words, and I am grateful to myself for practicing the vulnerability and courage necessary to find that healing.

There was power in the Synergy Publishing Group of writers and coaches and production magicians. I am grateful for Shana, Melisa, Kemisha, and Taylor. As a team you have contributed your super powers to my journey. I am also grateful to the amazing writers who show up on the second and fourth Wednesday of every month to scribble with me for two hours. Your energy, your inspiration, and your words have carried me forward. And I am grateful for Stefanie and Shelley who acted as early beta readers, shooting straight and cheering me on. Ladies, this is a different book because of you.

And finally I am grateful for the powerful support of my husband and children that made this healing endeavor possible. We are all better for it.

The light in me sees and honors the bright shining light in each and each and every one of you!

Namaste!

ABOUT THE AUTHOR

Photo by Wanda Koch

Cindy Urbanski is a wife and mom who loves cooking wholesome food, reading good books, traveling, and being in the woods or near the water with her husband and children. She is the lead writing coach for Synergy Publishing Group and a yoga instructor, both occupations that tap into her super power of helping people love on themselves. Sometimes she even follows her own best advice.

Cindy also loves talking to groups of all sizes and demographics about her books, her writing, and the messy process of writing. Her current focus is on getting as many voices out into the world as possible because people's stories matter and the telling of those stories is healing.

Connect with Cindy

🌐 cindyurbanski.com

📷 cindy_d_urbanski

✉️ cindy@cindyurbanski.com

Made in the USA
Columbia, SC
25 September 2024